FOOTPATHS FO

W
YORKSHIRE

Peter Young

COUNTRYSIDE BOOKS
NEWBURY BERKSHIRE

First published 2009
© Peter Young 2009

COUNTRYSIDE BOOKS
3 Catherine Road
Newbury, Berkshire

To view our complete range of books,
please visit us at
www.countrysidebooks.co.uk

ISBN: 978 1 84674 145 6

Maps by Gelder Design & Mapping
Photographs by the author

Designed by Peter Davies, Nautilus Design
Produced through MRM Associates Ltd., Reading
Typeset by CJWT Solutions, St Helens
Printed by Information Press, Oxford

CONTENTS

FOOTPATHS FOR FITNESS

GRADE 3 – HIKE

Introduction

After dinner, rest awhile,
After supper, walk a mile.
16th-century proverb

Perhaps you would like to feel fitter, or maybe you have been advised to take more exercise? If so, this book is for you, especially if you have not been in the habit of going out for walks!

The health benefits of taking a walk are well known; even short walks, if you undertake them regularly, can help you keep in trim. Walking is a natural form of exercise that is readily available to us, and it is cheap. Many people take their dogs for walks, which helps the owners keep fit. It seems right to walk with a dog but if you don't own one, then what? Some years ago I remember a colleague at work saying that she felt a bit 'spare' – a Yorkshire term – going out for a walk without a dog. That's a pity. You should not feel self-conscious doing a natural activity that is simple, basic and health-giving.

The routes in this book are graded according to distance and how challenging they are. The three groups are:

Grade 1 – STROLL

Grade 2 – STRIDE

Grade 3 – HIKE

Grade 1 **Strolls** are from just over 1 mile up to 3 miles long and generally fairly easy.

Grade 2 **Strides** are between 3 miles and just under 6 miles long, and some are more difficult.

Grade 3 **Hikes** are about 5 miles to 8 miles long and the most strenuous.

RELAX AND ENJOY THE OUTDOORS

These circuits are designed to help people not used to setting off for a ramble to find somewhere pleasant to walk, away from the routine of their home environment. In West Yorkshire we have a county with so many fascinating places to visit – you will find routes in all five of the districts, in areas with many things of interest to see and do.

We try to get away from the noise of traffic and towns to experience some peace and quiet. Let's hear birdsong and see rivers, trees, canals, castles, stately homes and reservoirs. The countryside should help you to feel more relaxed about enjoying your stroll, or stride or even a hike! Being out of doors in pleasant countryside is a good therapy, and it can stimulate the mind and body in a positive way.

WHAT ABOUT THE CALORIES?

Remember that walking *can* burn the calories off, if you go about it the right way. We should not pretend it is easy. Taking regular exercise is the key, which is often difficult, but it is worth making the effort.

Health professionals recommend that adults require at least 2½ hours of moderate intensity aerobic exercise – brisk walking for example – every week. By and large, most of us do not take enough exercise. You can do something about it, it's your body – your health! You burn calories by the amount of energy used in an activity. In walking your weight times the distance walked equals the calories burnt.

However, counting calories is not an exact science as there are several factors involved. The table gives some idea of the calories someone might burn in an hour's level walking:

Weight	8 stone 112 lbs 51 kilos	11 stone 154 lbs 70 kilos	17 stone 238 lbs 108 kilos	20 stone 280 lbs 127 kilos
Walking at 2 mph	160 calories	210 calories	240 calories	312 calories
Walking at 3 mph	210 calories	275 calories	320 calories	416 calories
Walking at 4½ mph	295 calories	390 calories	440 calories	572 calories

It shows that a person weighing 8 stone can burn around 160 calories by walking for an hour at 2 mph. A heavier person will burn more calories over the same time and speed. Going a bit faster can burn off more calories, and walking up a hill is good for you as well.

I should add that calories are put on by the amount of food we eat. If we consume more calories than we expend in exercise it inevitably means that the body retains the extra – as fat. But this is a walking book, not a cookery book!

WHAT TO TAKE

Be prepared for the weather. You need the right clothes, but you don't have to dress up to go walking. Nearly all of us have outdoor clothes suitable for the walks in this book. Of course, it is always best to take a waterproof and spare warm clothing. What is important is to have the right footwear, a key to enjoying a walk. Sturdy shoes or boots are best for most of the longer walks.

Take a snack, especially if children are with you, as they always look forward to a picnic. If you are wanting children to enjoy walking, then be subtle. Don't say they are going for a walk, call it an exploration or an expedition, or it's a journey to a particular place. It might also help to involve them in the planning. Well, you can always try.

The appropriate Ordnance Survey map is shown for each walk, and will add interest with the extra detail these maps contain. Finding a grid reference is clearly explained on OS maps in the information section.

METRO, TO GET YOU THERE

If public transport is appropriate to reach a location, the details are shown in the introduction to the walks. Why not try and make use of the rail and bus services? The majority of the starting points for the walks in the book can be reached by using the widespread transport network we have in West Yorkshire. Metro publish the *How to get around* maps, which have good information covering services in each district of the county. These are available from travel centres and stations. For bus and train times in West Yorkshire visit the website at www.wymetro.com or phone Metroline 0113 245 7676.

Enjoy the walks, enjoy West Yorkshire and enjoy feeling fitter.

Peter Young

Publisher's Note

We **hope that you obtain** considerable enjoyment from this book; great care has been taken in its preparation. Although at the time of publication all routes followed public rights of way or permitted paths, diversion orders can be made and permissions withdrawn.

We cannot, of course, be held responsible for such diversion orders and any inaccuracies in the text which result from these or any other changes to the routes nor any damage which might result from walkers trespassing on private property. We are anxious though that all details covering the walks are kept up to date and would therefore welcome information from readers which would be relevant to future editions.

The simple sketch maps that accompany the walks in this book are based on notes made by the author whilst checking out the routes on the ground. They are designed to show you how to reach the start, to point out the main features of the overall circuit and they contain a progression of numbers that relate to the paragraphs of the text.

However, for the benefit of a proper map, we do recommend that you purchase the relevant Ordnance Survey sheet covering your walk. The Ordnance Survey maps are widely available, especially through booksellers and local newsagents.

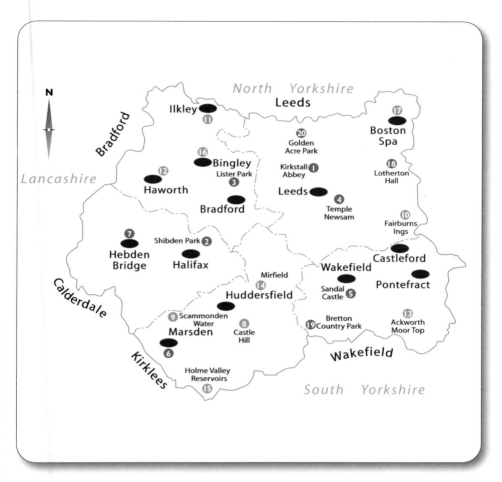

Area map showing location of the walks

Grade 1 – STROLL

Grade 2 – STRIDE

Grade 3 – HIKE

Kirkstall Abbey, Leeds
Get the Walking Habit

■ *A wonderful rural landscape and only 2 miles from Leeds city centre!* ■

The **extensive ruins of Kirkstall Abbey** are located in attractive grounds, and though this is an inner city area, the place has a rural feel with many trees and rolling grassland. Kirkstall was founded in 1152 and the buildings are still remarkably well preserved. The River Aire flows by, one reason that the monks came here in the first place. A modern visitor centre explains the story of the brothers and the buildings. There are activities for children and you can also visit the Abbey House Museum, where Victorian streets have been reconstructed.

1 Turn left out of the visitor centre and continue left, beyond the black bollards onto a wide path, with the grass on your right. The ruins of the abbey, which you pass, have information boards explaining what the buildings were. A fence prevents access along here, but tours are available. From the end of the buildings continue ahead on the wide path, now climbing a little. You may see a weir across the **River Aire** to the right. Reach an entrance to the grounds where a signpost points ahead to the **Wild Flower Meadow**, **Bridge Road** and **Goitside Walk**.

2 Continue ahead on a narrower path to another entrance and turn right at a grass triangle. Go down to a wooden footbridge and cross the goit, which carries water from the river. Turn left and reach the wild flower meadow. There is a seat and a notice board explaining the field. There should be something of interest at most times of the year. You can continue on the path to **Bridge Road** and see the local war memorial. You may also notice the miniature railway.

3 Go back on the track and over the footbridge. Turn left at the grass triangle and return along the path, only as far as the first turning left. Before the signpost for the **Goitside Walk** seen earlier, a path goes down to a gateway and a second bridge. You can have a view of the weir from around here. Note the end of the railway line nearby.

> **GRADE: 1**
> **ESTIMATED CALORIE BURN: 220**
>
> **Description:** An enjoyable stroll in a small green area.
> **Distance:** 1¼ miles
> **Time:** 1 hour
> **Gradient:** Mostly level, but you will find some slopes.
> **Underfoot:** Surfaced paths around the abbey grounds and a grassy riverside section, which can be muddy after rain; no stiles.
> **Starting point:** Kirkstall Abbey visitor centre. GR 260362.
> **How to get there:** Kirkstall Abbey is on the A65, about 2 miles from Leeds city centre. Park in the free car park at the Abbey House Museum, across the A65 from the abbey. There are frequent buses from Leeds bus station.
> **OS map:** Explorer 289 Leeds or 288 Bradford & Huddersfield.
> **Refreshments:** The Abbey House Museum.

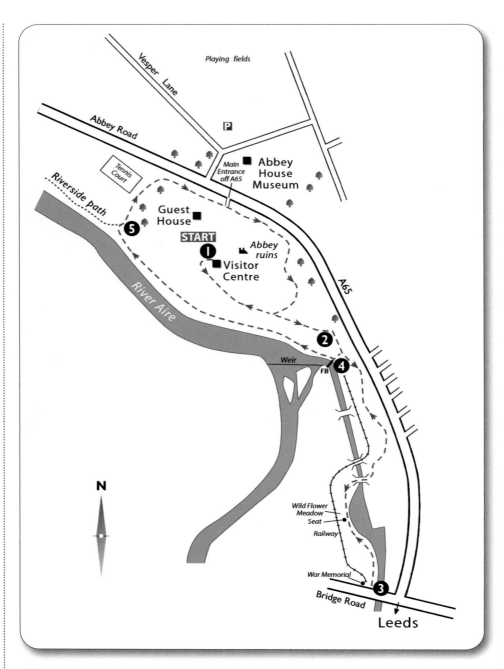

■ *The ruined Kirkstall Abbey was once a flourishing monastic house* ■

4 To the right of the gateway, as you face it, drop down to a grassy path, which you follow beside the river. As you walk there are views across the grounds of the extensive remains of the abbey. The track is unsurfaced and may be muddy at times. It is good that there is fine riverside scenery so near to the city centre. Keep on to reach a surfaced path and take a right turn. Ahead are sports fields and there is a signed **Riverside Walk**. You can extend the walk here, if you wish, but the path can tend to get overgrown, the further you go.

5 Continue on the surfaced track as for the **Abbey House Museum**. Try going up the slope briskly. On the right you see the remains of the **Guest House**, which once catered for visitors. Continue past the main entrance to the grounds, but you need not turn down to the visitor centre yet. For a final circuit of the buildings go ahead on a narrower path, on the left of the abbey church. Follow this round and below the east end of the church and then beside a fence. Keep going and join the wider track you used at the start. Go right on it and return to the visitor centre with a good pace.

Shibden Park, Halifax
Five Hundred Years of History

FOOTPATHS
FOR FITNESS

■ *Shibden Hall has welcomed visitors for centuries* ■

Think of a typically English, half-timbered and substantial manor house, set amongst fine trees and extensive parkland, and you have Shibden Hall. Built around 1420, it was occupied by the Lister family for 300 years. The striking frontage will impress you and, if you have time, you can visit the interior to see how people used to live. There are several paths around the park and walking here provides plenty of interest, while getting exercise. Many of the facilities have been refurbished and, with a new visitor centre, it is a good time to visit. There is a boating lake and you may be there when the miniature railway is running. Children will also like the play area. Entry to the park is free but there is a charge to visit the hall.

1 From the visitor centre go left towards the lake and turn left before it on the first track. Turn right along the path on the left side of the lake – **The Mere**. The miniature railway runs in the grassed area on the left. Reach the end of the lake, where the boating takes place. From a short balustrade, steps go down to a wooded area, but do not go there yet – later perhaps (see point 5). Take a wide track going up, which climbs to the children's play area. Go through, bearing left and leave by a yellow gate.

2 Keep ahead on the track, and join another coming in from the right. Continue here, signed as 'Way Out', and cross the middle of the park between the open grassland. To the left **Shibden Hall** is seen above. Ignore a right turning halfway along and reach the road to the visitor centre. Cross this and go right briefly, then sharp left and up a path beside the road. When you reach a large stone building you see a narrower path on the left, signed to **Shibden Hall and Gardens**.

3 Cross the road and take this winding and unsurfaced path up through trees. In a few minutes there are displays of stonework to examine. The area shows examples of stone walls, pillars and cairns as well as a sheepfold. Try and find the 'lunky'! Continue up and go left into the disabled parking area, with toilets. Keep by the low wall and on the sanded area, where you reach **Shibden Hall**.

4 At the front of the hall the formal gardens and the views over the grounds are renowned. From the flagpole corner walk to the end of the long

GRADE: 1
ESTIMATED CALORIE BURN: 280

Description: Something of interest round every corner.
Distance: 1¼ miles
Time: 1 hour
Gradient: Rolling parkland with some steep slopes.
Underfoot: Mostly surfaced paths, and a few rougher tracks; no stiles.
Starting point: The visitor centre, where there is free parking. GR 107261.
How to get there: Shibden Hall is on the A58, a mile from Halifax. Buses 548 and 549 from Halifax are frequent.
OS map: Explorer 288 Bradford & Huddersfield.
Refreshments: Shibden Hall and the visitor centre.

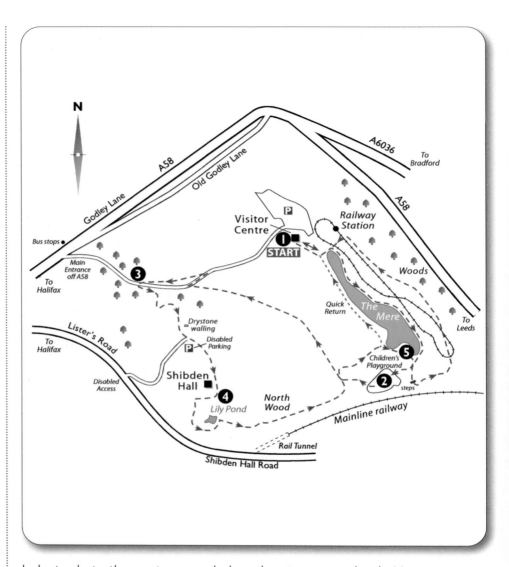

balustrade to the next corner, below the steep grass bank. You can go up the steps for other views of the hall and gardens. The route continues on the path going left down steps to the **Lily Pond**, which you see below. This area is the **Wilderness**, laid out by Anne Lister in the 19th century. From the pond turn right, down an unsurfaced track through **North Wood**. Put on a bit of speed here, perhaps, through a darker section. Join the path from

■ *Extensive grounds in the park provide a good stroll* ■

the children's playground and go left, then right and down to reach the boating area again.

For a quick return to your start, go along the path on the left of the lake, which brings you back to the visitor centre.

5 *For a little more exercise and to see more of the park*, look for the steps you passed in point 1 at the end of the lake. Go down these, or down the slope to the right. Follow the sanded path to the left, over a stone bridge and cross the railway track. The path is paved and you go into the wood a little way. Keep on the path, which rises then falls, passing the miniature railway and picnic area. Come out of the wood near the railway station and you will see the visitor centre not far away.

■ *Lister Park is a fine place to walk and talk* ■

Lister Park is close to the centre of Bradford and it is a popular green oasis for the city. Recent refurbishments, helped by Lottery money, have made it an appealing venue and at present the park is looking in fine condition. In summer the wide areas of grass attract sunseekers. After walking round a perimeter drive, which encircles the park, you follow a meandering route to see many of its points of interest. Joggers use the easy paths and you should be able to walk off some calories amongst surprisingly good scenery. The outstanding building of Cartwright Hall displays a variety of artistic exhibitions. Although the hall is not really included in this walk, you can obtain here a good guide to Lister Park to accompany this description.

1 The route starts at the traffic entrance off **North Park Road** opposite **Selbourne Villas**, and at first does a circuit along most of the inner driveway around the park. There is only light traffic. You pass each pedestrian entrance to the park so it is possible to start the walk at these points also. You see some of the park's features, which you can return to later.

Go left from the entrance, on the wide drive. Before the gate ahead from **Emm Lane**, turn right on the right of a triangular grass area. As you walk down you see the circular **Fossil Tree** on your right, and you return to this later. Continue down to the **Norman Arch** and turn right at the **statue of Sir Titus Salt**.

2 Keep on the perimeter drive with the busy **Manningham Lane** away on your left. You pass the boating lake and in the pavilion there are toilets. Keep on the drive, seeing **Cartwright Hall** above on the right. Continue ahead towards a gate at the **Oak Lane** entrance; there are toilets here. You pass an imposing **statue of Samuel Cunliffe Lister** and make a sharp turn right on the drive, which now slopes up. Soon reach the impressive entrance

GRADE: 1
ESTIMATED CALORIE BURN: 340

Description: A fine urban park with many features.
Distance: 2 miles
Time: 1¼ hours
Gradient: Sloping land and only a few steep areas.
Underfoot: Paved and clear paths; no stiles.
Starting point: The free car park at the Bowling Pavilion entrance, off North Park Road. GR 150351.
How to get there: Lister Park is on the A650, Manningham Lane, one mile from the centre of Bradford. Turn off Manningham Lane onto Oak Lane and take the first right immediately into North Park Road. Several bus routes run past the park.
OS map: Explorer 288 Bradford & Huddersfield.
Refreshments: Café at the boating lake.

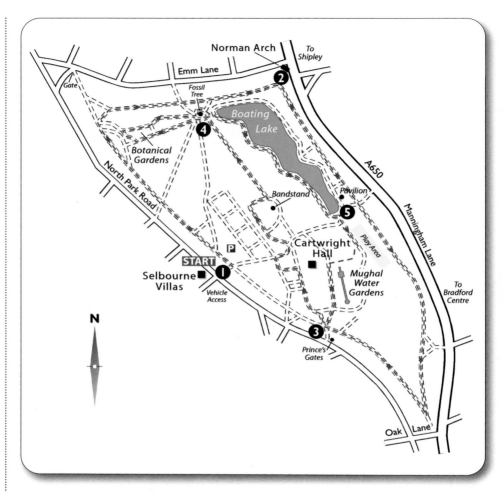

known as the **Prince's Gates** and you leave the driveway circuit. You have walked about 1¼ miles.

3 Turn right towards **Cartwright Hall**, with flower beds in front of it. Now go to the left of the hall, on a route to see the inner parts of **Lister Park**. There is a floral clock on the left; then go up the steps into the **Garden Wall Gallery**, which often has pictures by visiting children. Go past the fine carving of a stag, then through the bollards and to the right. Go down and round on a wide path, into a long area with a balustrade. Drop down to the bandstand below, where the names of composers are carved in the stone.

■ *The boating lake* ■

Take the path away from the bandstand. Pass the **Meteorological Station** and reach the **Fossil Tree**.

4 On the left here you access the **Botanical Gardens**, which run up and around the stream. The park's own guide is useful here, listing over 20 trees and features. If you can, make more than one circuit of the area – you could try and walk on every path as there is some uphill walking involved. When you are ready, continue the route from the **Fossil Tree**. Go on the narrow path signed to the **Boating Pavilion** and reach the lakeside. Go either left or right around the lake, then reach the end, near the pavilion.

5 From the end of the lake cross an open area and go ahead on the path, with the children's play area on your left. Turn first right up the steps towards the hall and on your left admire the **Mughal Water Gardens**. By now you should be familiar with the layout of the park and will be able to reach the car park area or other exit.

Temple Newsam
The Pride of Leeds

■ *Springtime at Temple Newsam* ■

Leeds is justly proud of its 1,500 acre estate at Temple Newsam, with the centrepiece a magnificent Tudor-Jacobean restored mansion. The estate is explained in publications at the shop. Nearby is Home Farm, which once provided for the family and a large number of estate workers. Now it is an experience designed for visitors to get close to the animals and take part in traditional farming crafts. The spacious grounds of Temple Newsam provide scope for good short walks. You can enjoy the gardens as well as the views of the rolling parkland.

1 From the entrance to **Home Farm** go down the path with the red-brick wall on your left. Turn left onto the wide road, but only for a few yards. Go left again onto a narrower track, signed as the **Pink and Blue health walks**. A little further on, continue at a signpost to the **Walled Garden**; the **Sphinx Gates** are on the left. Continue down the path and on the right see the ha-ha, a sunken ditch that acts as a fence. The lake comes into view ahead and you follow the path to the left. Reach the first wooden footbridge and cross a stream. There are ducks and swans on the water and the trees are attractive in most seasons.

2 *Here the routes divide. The longer walk continues at point 5. The shorter walk goes right, following a sign indicating an 'Easy Going Route'. After a few yards turn first left, and then right. The going is up, and the surface is not smooth. Perhaps you are feeling a little warmer, as you look down on the lake. Keep on, turning left on an Easy Going Route, up a track that curves to the right and climbs. In a few minutes arrive at the* **Little Temple** *and* **Temple Newsam House** *is seen from here.*

3 It was once fashionable to provide viewpoints such as this, though it is now in need of restoration. Follow the footpath signed to the **Lakes**, and go down to the right at the next turning. This part may be muddy after rain. You walk between trees and go down fairly steadily. Descending can burn

GRADE: 1
ESTIMATED CALORIE BURN: 200/340

Description: Fine grounds make a good location.
Distance: 1¼ or 2¼ miles
Time: ¾ hour or 1½ hours
Gradient: Descents and a climb to a viewpoint. No stiles on the shorter walk; 6 on the longer walk, which can be shortened.
Underfoot: Surfaced paths in the central area, unsurfaced on the longer walk.
Starting point: By the entrance to Home Farm. Toilets nearby. GR 359323.
How to get there: Temple Newsam is 4 miles from Leeds centre and is signed off the A63. From the M1, turn off at junction 46. Charge for the house car park; other car parks free.
OS map: Explorer 289 Leeds.
Refreshments: In the Stable Courtyard.

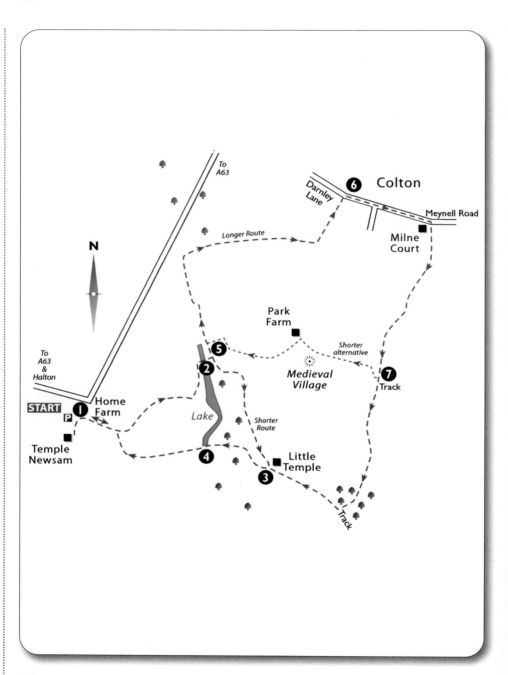

To A63

Colton 6

Darnley Lane

Meynell Road

Milne Court

N

Longer Route

Park Farm

To A63 & Halton

Shorter alternative

5

Medieval Village

2

7 Track

START

Home Farm

Lake

Temple Newsam

Shorter Route

4

Little Temple

3

Track

■ *Temple Newsam House is surrounded by plenty of parkland* ■

calories as well as climbing up, because there is exertion involved, of a different sort. Soon you are down to the water and you cross a footbridge. Go ahead to a road junction.

4 Now walk up on the wide surfaced road, though there is unlikely to be any traffic. This is a gradual climb, with seats around. Why not try to do it quickly? As you walk, the 'big house' comes into view across the rolling parkland. Some of the trees were originally planned by 'Capability' Brown to provide what he considered a perfect landscape. Maybe you will notice the other end of the ha-ha. You will see the red brick wall of **Home Farm** as you continue steadily up. Go left towards the front of **Temple Newsam House** to study the extraordinary façade, before returning to the starting point.

5 *The longer route goes left from the bridge.* Follow the **Pink Route** along the path, passing the **Walled Garden** to the right, then briefly left and right

25

onto a level path, a **Pink Route**. You see this curving ahead to the right. Follow it, and before reaching a gate there is a footpath sign pointing right to **Colton**. Go up steps and over a stile, then slightly left up a field to a second stile. Go right on a path inside a fence. Turn left at the end, walking past houses to reach the end of **Darnley Lane** at a T-junction. You are at **Colton**.

6 Go to the right in **Colton Road** and cross a road into **Meynell Road**. After **Milne Court** go right at a footpath sign. Follow this enclosed footpath, crossing a metal footbridge, and keep on to a wooden stile where a wider track crosses the path.

7 *You can shorten the walk here.* Go right and follow the track round to the right and left to reach **Park Farm**. Go over the stile, or the unusual bridleway gate, to see the board that explains **Colton Medieval Village**. Continue on the footpath to the **Lakes**, with the **Walled Garden** across to the right. You will recognise the lake area when you reach it.

To continue the longer walk, cross the track onto the path signed to **Wilderness Woods**. Go ahead, then towards the end of the field bear a little left to a metal gate into the woods. Follow the path through and reach a wide track. Turn right on this a few yards to reach another track, at a corner. Go through a metal gate and follow a sign opposite, to the **Little Temple**. You reach this in a few minutes. *Now continue on the shorter route from point 3.* This came to the Little Temple the opposite way, and you retrace your steps for a few yards.

Sandal Castle, Wakefield

FOOTPATHS FOR FITNESS

Days of Wars and Roses

■ *The gentle path leading to the remains of Sandal Castle* ■

When you climb to the keep of the 13th century Sandal Castle the view is unrivalled. Though much of the once mighty building has gone, it has not stopped archaeologists from being able to describe how the castle looked in its heyday. It experienced real history in 1460 during the Wars of the Roses when the English Crown was at stake, and its role is well explained at the visitor centre. Nearby there is Pugneys Country Park, and added to this is a nature reserve, where hides allow you to observe the birdlife on the water. Take binoculars for a better view.

GRADE: 1
ESTIMATED CALORIE BURN: 340

Description: Walk from a historic castle and round the lake of a country park.
Distance: 2½ miles
Time: 1¾ hours
Gradient: Fairly level around the lake, but the castle is on a high point; 2 stiles.
Underfoot: The paths are generally easy.
Starting point: The visitor centre at Sandal Castle where there is currently free parking and toilet facilities. GR 338181.
How to get there: Sandal Castle is signed off the A61, Barnsley Road, south of the centre of Wakefield. Buses pass nearby and Sandal & Agbrigg station on the Wakefield line is 15 minutes away.
OS map: Explorer 278 Sheffield & Barnsley.
Refreshments: At Pugneys centre.

1 Before you start, cross the bridge over the moat and climb the steps to the viewpoint at **Sandal Castle**, where the keep once stood. The M1 motorway is seen beyond the lake of **Pugneys Country Park**. Its centre building stands by the lake. When you have taken in the view, go back down the steps. Turn left on the path, which circles round, and back to the visitor centre.

To start the walk, go to the right from the visitor centre, down the path and through the car park. Leave through the gateway and go left on the pavement. Walk a few yards to the corner, where the road turns right. Here a narrow path goes off, slightly left, between hedges. Follow this and when the hedge turns left, continue straight ahead down the open path over fields. The land on the right was the scene of the Battle of Wakefield, which was fought on 30th December 1460. Reach a corner, near modern houses, and turn left onto a track. This has hedges alongside it, and you follow it until it bends a little to the left. Leave it and go right on a path along a field edge, to a track. Cross this and go left on a footbridge over a stream. In a few yards you join a good track above the lake.

2 Here you go right, keeping on the track going round the lake – a chance to quicken your pace, perhaps. This and the other stretches of water you see were formed by open-cast mining and quarrying. On the lake there will often be water activities taking place. Keep on the track and the buildings of **Pugneys centre** come into view ahead. Before it you pass an area of

exercise possibilities. You could try push-pull boards, step-up poles or maybe a Tai Chi pathway. From the exercise area you could leave the track and go nearer the lake to walk below the car park. Reach the centre, which has some facilities. The main road ahead is the A636, **Denby Dale Road**. Across the lake **Sandal Castle** is seen on the skyline.

3 From the centre continue on the track round the lake, now unsurfaced. Soon you see a narrow gauge railway, the **Pugneys Light Railway**. This is

■ *Looking across the lake* ■

run by enthusiasts and you may be here at a time when it is running. Don't rely on it though, you are here for a walk! Continue round and just after the rail track turns off, a bird hide is signed. You can make an interesting short detour to the nature reserve area, and look out from the hide over a lake that is separate to the main one. Return to this point and keep going on the path, with occasional seats. Another hide is situated where both lakes are in sight. The path comes out, clear of trees and there is a sign on the right indicating a pathway to **Sandal Castle**.

4 Walk along the path, which bears down to the right, and join a long boardwalk. At the end cross a concrete footbridge and go ahead on a path beside the hedge. Reach the buildings of **Castle Farm** and go right on the track, then almost immediately left over a stile, by a metal gate. Follow this track up towards the castle between fields, passing through a gap into the left hand field. Continue up and bear left at the top of the field to a stile, hardly needed. Enter the castle area and go up the grass onto the track. A right turn brings you to the visitor centre. Why not make another visit to the castle viewpoint where you can trace the route you have walked?

6 Marsden

Men Are From Marsden

FOOTPATHS
FOR FITNESS

■ *Tunnel End at Marsden* ■

In times past, **Marsden** was a rather inaccessible place, with its people known for an independence of mind. The Pennine village was a centre of activity by the Luddites, who destroyed the new machinery they saw as taking their jobs. Nowadays many visitors to Marsden come to see Tunnel End on the Huddersfield Narrow Canal, the entrance to the 3¼ mile long Standedge Tunnel. This wonder of the inland waterway system is the highest, deepest and longest canal tunnel in Britain. Originally the barges were propelled through it by the bargees pushing with their feet, in darkness. You can go inside by electric boat. Children will be thrilled by the sight of trains rushing out of the railway tunnel adjacent to the canal.

31

1 Below the railway station, follow the signs for '**Towpath Walk to Tunnel End**'. This goes along the left bank of the **Huddersfield Narrow Canal** on a level walk of ½ mile. Reach an area where the dark, forbidding mouth of the tunnel is seen. Beside it are **Tunnel End Cottages** where the boat trips start, and a modern visitor centre is over the road. There are picnic areas and usually an air of bustle. You will return here after a short stroll!

2 The walk continues past the visitor centre entrance and up the drive. At the top see the **Tunnel End Inn** and go left on the lane, **Waters Road**, a few yards to a wooden gate on the left. From the gate turn right on a path with a firm surface, which winds ahead, easy walking. The reservoir that feeds the canal is nearby. The path reaches a second gate where you rejoin **Waters Road**. You have walked about one mile. Go left on the road, pass the houses of **Lower Hey Green** and see an unusual carved gate on the right. This is the **Hey Green Hotel Sculpture Gate** by Jason Thompson, a modern work, which depicts the story of the Hey Green's historical connection with the South Pacific. Beside the road the **River Colne** has some fine waterfalls. Reach a junction, with the **Hey Green Hotel** nearby, and a footpath signed to **Lower Green Owlers**. Before you go up steps to a small gate, check the next point.

GRADE: 1
ESTIMATED CALORIE BURN: 480

Description: A good introduction to the area, including the Standedge Tunnel.

Distance: 2¾ miles

Time: 2 hours

Gradient: Most of the walking around Marsden is rugged. There are ups and downs with some short, steep sections; 3 stiles.

Underfoot: Canal paths, quiet roads and unsurfaced tracks; these can be tricky and wet, so boots are advisable.

Starting point: Near the National Trust car park entrance, below Marsden railway station at the top of Station Road. GR 047118. Toilets in the village and at Tunnel End.

How to get there: Marsden is 12 miles west of Huddersfield, on the A62. Park in the free National Trust car park adjacent to the railway station. Rail service from Huddersfield and Leeds.

OS map: OL21 South Pennines.

Refreshments: At Tunnel End, also pubs and cafés in Marsden.

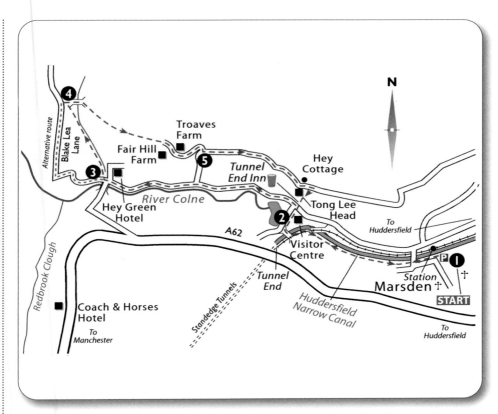

3 *In wet conditions the land above the steps can be very muddy.* You can continue ahead on **Blake Lea Lane**. Keep on up this steep lane, round bends and passing properties. The views around you are very impressive. Reach a metal gate on the right with two signposts, the highest spot of the walk. Go through the gate and follow the higher sign as in point 4.

In dry conditions, go up the steps and through the gate then continue up by the wall. This is suddenly steep climbing and hard work, but there is not very much of it. Cross a wooden stile and keep up, following a line of ancient stones. From a second stile there is a slightly precarious short stretch, then you climb the hillside. Aim up towards electricity posts. Reach a metal gate by a road with two footpath signs, and turn right here. This is the highest spot of the walk, and the exertion may have made you warm.

4 Follow the higher sign, on a path going down quite steeply, to a wooden footbridge over a moorland stream. Continue up on the path, climbing to

33

■ *A distant view of Marsden* ■

a plateau. The route ahead is obvious and you enjoy good views as you follow the contour of the hillside, repaying the effort of getting up here. There are still ups and downs as the narrow path winds ahead, with occasional boardwalks. As you approach a house, go down to a wall before it. There is a narrow path on the left of the property, **Fair Hill Farm**, which you walk along, then bear right and down. Go left on a concrete drive – see the arrow on a post. From the next property, **Troaves Farm**, keep on a lane and go down to a T-junction.

5 Turn left at a footpath sign. Go up the track on a straight section and keep on it, passing houses and buildings. Look for **Hey Cottage** on the left, then soon reach a property on the right, **Tong Lee Head**. The name is seen when you look back. A few yards ahead, turn right between two old stone gateposts, where a path descends steeply. There are steps going through a garden, clearly signed, but do not linger here. From a wooden stile go down to the **Tunnel End Inn**. Cross the road into the canal area once again. Return to the start by the towpath. There is a wider path going parallel on the right of the towpath. You can follow this to emerge a little way down **Station Road** in **Marsden**.

Hebden Bridge
Walkers Are Welcome

FOOTPATHS FOR FITNESS

■ *The Rochdale canal flows through the town* ■

Hebden Bridge is set in the steep-sided Calder valley and this interesting town prides itself on being the 'centre of the universe' – according to a carved stone in the town. 'Funky' and 'quirky' are some other descriptions used. Its green credentials are genuine, with an Alternative Technology Centre and several green shops. It was the first 'Walkers are Welcome' town; one requirement is to have at least three clear walking routes in good condition. The steep climb to the ancient hilltop village of Heptonstall should burn off a few calories.

35

GRADE: 1
ESTIMATED CALORIE BURN: 300/375

Description: Picturesque strolls in Calderdale.
Distance: 1½ or 3 miles
Time: 1½ or 2¼ hours
Gradient: A steep climb features at the start; no stiles.
Underfoot: The hillside paths are generally narrow and need care.
Starting point: The canal marina in Hebden Bridge, near the tourist office. Five minutes from the railway station. Toilets opposite. GR 993271.
How to get there Hebden Bridge is on the A646 between Halifax and Todmorden. There is fee paying parking near the marina, and some free on-street parking. Good rail service on the Caldervale line.
OS map: OL21 South Pennines.
Refreshments: Plenty of choice.

1 From the canal marina turn left on the main road and walk past the cinema to the traffic lights. Go over into **Bridge Gate** and in the pedestrian zone look for the fine packhorse bridge, which you will cross. You can first take in the scene around **St George's Square**, where in good weather there is a Continental feel as people sit outside at tables. Cross the packhorse bridge and the way you go is up the steep, cobbled lane ahead, signed as the footpath to **Heptonstall**. Known as the **Buttress**, at first the slope is around 25%. Just take your time. Join a road and go right, and after about 200 yards a footpath is signed across the road. More climbing is needed, up steps and following a paved path to another road. Turn right and a steady gradient brings you to **Heptonstall**, with its stone setts. At **Hepton Drive** there is a small garden, and the seats here will be welcome too.

2 The route continues on **Church Lane**, and up the steps into the area of the old and new churches. The number of gravestones is remarkable. You might want to explore the historic village. The numerous windows in many of the old houses were to allow maximum light for the weavers to work. The 1642 grammar school is now the museum.

To continue the walk, turn right from the north door of the modern church and follow the building round to the east wall. Go down steps to rejoin **Church Lane**. You are almost at a junction, and the route continues ahead, past **West Laithe**. A diversion a few yards right, on the wide track, leads to a burial area containing the grave of the American poetess Sylvia

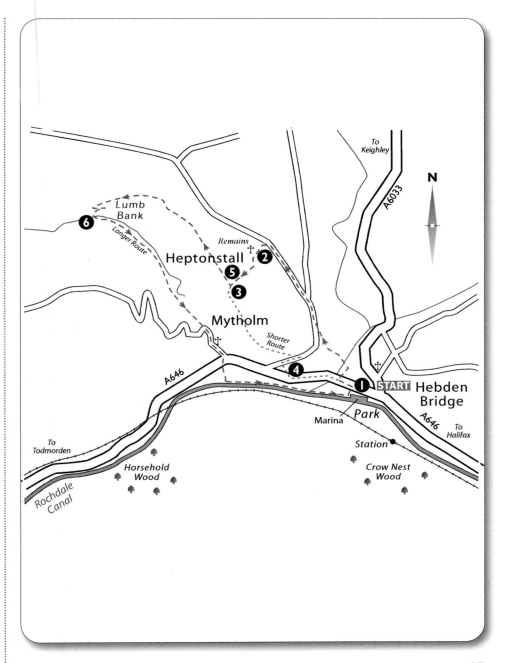

Plath. She was the wife of former Poet Laureate Ted Hughes, who was born in nearby Mytholmroyd. She died young, and tragically, and her grave is regularly visited by admirers of her work. The grave is situated in the front left-hand area.

From **West Laithe**, the track crosses a road and turns right at a footpath sign to **Colden**. Follow an enclosed lane to a gap, where suddenly a splendid vista of the valley is revealed. To the south the monument at **Stoodley Pike** is seen.

3 *Here the routes divide. The longer route turns right and is described at point 5.*

For the shorter route, go down on the path ahead, steep at first but mostly clear. There are steps and stony sections. Care is needed, and the exertion probably equals the amount of climbing earlier. The large rocks you see are called **Hell Hole**. The path bears left and becomes less steep as it contours round the hillside. The way through trees is very pleasant and you look down on the world. Reach **Heptonstall Road** and turn right. Cross over and pass **Queens Terrace**, then a few yards ahead go left at a gap and down a series of steps. These are the **Cuckoo Steps**, quite tricky to descend. At the end, when you join the road you have walked down **Stoney Lane**. Turn left into the bustle of **Hebden Bridge** and you can continue to the marina.

4 If you still have the energy, however, a short extension by the **Rochdale Canal** is enjoyable. Go over the zebra crossing at the junction of **Hangingroyd Road** and **Market Street**. Walk to the south along **Hebble End** and go left on the canal path. Reach the **Alternative Technology Centre**, then cross an aqueduct over the **Calder**. Continue to **bridge 16a**, to return to the marina.

5 *For the longer route,* turn right from the gap at the end of point 2 and walk on this fine high-level path. You weave about through rocky parts and trees. It should be good exercise. After a clearer section, emerge on a surfaced lane and bear left towards **Lumb Mill**. Soon pass **Lumb Bank** and the bridleway becomes unsurfaced. Take a sharp bend left, passing the sign to **Colden Clough** on the right. Go down the track towards the property of **Lower Lumb**, bearing right before it and going down to the bridge over **Colden Water**.

6 Turn left, passing the chimney, and follow the unsurfaced lane for about ¾ mile down to **Mytholm**, perhaps with extra speed. Reach the built-up area,

■ *A busy scene in Hebden Bridge* ■

with the church on your left. Continue to the main road and cross by the refuge. Almost immediately, pass through a gap at the bridge on the right of the stream. Go down steps to a path beside the stream and cross the river by a footbridge. Go ahead to the canal and turn left on an interesting section. Reach the **Alternative Technology Centre**, then cross an aqueduct over the **Calder**. Continue to **bridge 16a**, to return to the marina.

39

8 Castle Hill

Huddersfield's Point of View

■ *Extensive views from Castle Hill* ■

Castle Hill has long been one of West Yorkshire's best known landmarks. In 1897 the residents of Huddersfield marked Queen Victoria's Diamond Jubilee, in style. A tower 100 feet tall was built on top of the town's local hill, which itself stands around 950 feet high. It is a popular spot, and there are usually people about, taking in the widespread views. On this walk, which starts from the tower, there is varied scenery in the countryside around and of course Castle Hill keeps coming into view. There is an extra ½ mile if you want to visit the village of Farnley Tyas.

1 From the front of the **Victoria Tower** go left down to the new sandy path. Follow it to the right and pass two seats. Go right and left up steps to a higher path. Follow this round the grass area to a road, which accesses the car park. Go over and continue on a track slightly lower down. Reach a flight of stone steps crossing the path. Go down these to a road. Turn left past a parking area and continue down **Lumb Lane**.

2 Almost immediately go left on a lane marked as a footpath and 'Unsuitable for Vehicles'. After 100 yards turn left up a signed narrow path, which goes through trees and above a property. Go through a stone gap and turn right down to a wooden stile. Reach a second stile, from where you walk down the left side of a field to a stile at a lane. Cross it and go down stone steps into a field. Follow the left hand edge to a second field. Follow the trees on the left and go down to a step stile at a road, **Lumb Lane**. Go left for a few yards and take the **Kirkburton Parish Council walk**, and public footpath signs. Walk down and bear right on the signed path, not quite as the OS map shows the footpath, going diagonally down to a stream, **Lumb Dike**. The plank footbridge is perhaps the lowest level of the walk. Climb the steps to a stand-alone stile and go ahead, neither right nor left. Soon reach a stile where you leave the wood.

3 Continue ahead by the field edge, with the boundary fence on the right. There are now views of **Castle Hill** from here and on later sections. Go

GRADE: 2
ESTIMATED CALORIE BURN: 650

Description: Enjoyable scenery, keeping Castle Hill in sight.
Distance: 3½ miles
Time: 2½ hours
Gradient: With a start at a high point, the route descends and climbs back to it.
Underfoot: Field paths and woodland tracks; 15 main stiles.
Starting point: The Victoria Tower. GR 152140.
How to get there: Castle Hill is about 2½ miles south-east of the centre of Huddersfield on Ashes Lane. From the A616 at Berry Brow, by the Golden Fleece pub, take Robin Hood Hill onto Park Lane and along Ashes Lane. There is free parking near Victoria Tower.
OS map: Explorer 288 Bradford & Huddersfield.
Refreshments: There is a pub in Farnley Tyas.

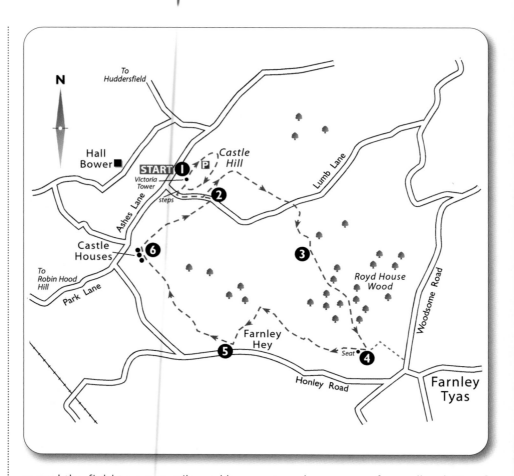

round the field to a gap stile and here enter a large area of woodland, **Royd House Wood**. The footpath crosses streams as it winds through. After the path goes through more open woodland you climb to a stile and leave the wood. Climb up the left hand edge of the field, which is quite steep. At the top there is a narrow path, which joins a track. Here you turn right through a gate and into a field, with a seat ahead, and you have walked over 1½ miles. *If you wish,* you can instead turn left, for **Farnley Tyas**. Follow the track and go right up to the village about ¼ mile away, where there is a pub. If you do this, return to the same spot.

4 Now continue down the field to a stile in the corner. Follow a series of paths by the wall through stiles and along field edges in a more or less continuous

■ *Castle Hill seen from afar* ■

line. The walking is generally level; try and keep moving fairly briskly on this section to achieve the calorie burn. From a wall corner cross the next field and reach a line of woodland to a stile. Cross an old lane and continue on an enclosed track to a sturdy stile with a **Kirkburton PCC** marker. Go up beside the field edge to a wall stile, then diagonally across the field to the buildings. Continue up a narrow passageway into a yard. Turn left onto a drive, passing the houses on the right. You are at **Farnley Hey**.

5 After the last house, and before the road, go right at a gap. Continue ahead and reach a post with a **KPCC** sign. Go slightly right and over a field to a wall. At a stile leave the **Kirkburton route**, which goes off right, along the wall. Carry on to **Castle Houses** ahead. As you reach the buildings, go on a track to the right behind a large barn. Turn right on a green lane.

6 **Castle Hill** is ahead and you go over the first stile, not to the right. Keep on in the field, and through stiles in the fields ahead. Approach a white cottage where you turn left onto the lane. Go up and you will recognise the **Lumb Lane** area, from where you set out. Return to **Castle Hill**, and the **Victoria Tower** to burn off those calories.

9 Scammonden Water
A Taste of the Wild

■ *Surveying the scene* ■

Thousands of people drive on the M62 between Leeds and Manchester and look down on Scammonden Water. The motorway crosses a dam constructed over a valley, and the stream of Black Burne Brook forms a reservoir. This walk encircles Scammonden and goes to a higher reservoir at Deanhead. With many trees planted, it is a pleasant valley in which to walk, with good Pennine views. The head of the valley is peaceful and you walk away from the sound of the motorway traffic. The walking is hard enough in places to ensure that the effort burns calories.

1 Start the walk from the far end of the car park, going through a gap by a gate. Continue on the path ahead, then turn left, on a track winding down through trees to reach the water's edge. The route continues left on the path by the reservoir.

Before you continue, go right towards the dam to an open area with seats and the valve tower. You will see the plaque that commemorates the inauguration of **Scammonden Reservoir** by the Queen in 1971. Leave this area, and with the motorway behind you, set off on the path beside the water. Walk along a narrow but clear path, with good views across the water. There will be birdlife on the reservoir and in the trees. A path joins from the left and you keep on to reach a hedge, which is the boundary of the sailing centre.

2 Go left up a signed '**Yorkshire Water Permissive Path**', narrow at times and climbing quite steeply for a few minutes. The path goes round the trees and up to a stile. A track, the **Kirklees Way** (KW), joins from the left. Leave the fence and go ahead towards trees and above the **Sailing Centre**. There is a boardwalk and a footbridge. Reach the car park of the centre and go left. Follow **KW** signs and turn sharply right by the first gate. Go down the track towards the reservoir and reach a

GRADE: 2
ESTIMATED CALORIE BURN: 720

Description: Good walking by a familiar viewpoint, in remote country.
Distance: 4½ miles
Time: 3¼ hours
Gradient: Rolling land with ups and downs.
Underfoot: Narrow paths in places, virtually no roads; 7 stiles.
Starting point: Wood Edge free car park. GR 055164.
How to get there: From the eastbound M62, leave at junction 23 and take the A640 signed to Rochdale. Turn off second right after the road crosses the motorway. Travelling westwards on the M62, there is no exit west from junction 23 so continue to junction 24 and take the A643, Lindley Moor Road, parallel with the motorway to junction 23. Take the A640 signed to Rochdale and follow directions as already stated.
OS map: OL21 South Pennines.
Refreshments: The Jack o' Mitre and Lower Royal George pubs are on the A640 nearby (New Hey Road).

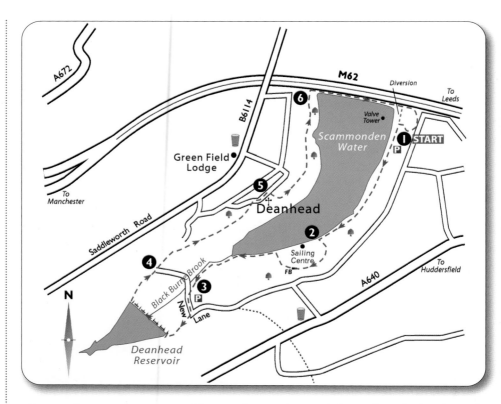

slipway by an open area. The path continues left and includes boards and two stiles as you make your way towards the top of the reservoir on a path winding through trees. Reach a field and see **New Lane car park**.

3 Go left up the lane and where it bends go to the right over the stile. A roughish track over open land leads up to the dam at **Deanhead Reservoir**, which gives fine views of the upper valley beyond the water. This walking is strenuous enough to give the exercise required and here you have lost the sound and sight of the motorway. Cross the metal bridge and go over the dam. Leave it at the far end and go right. Follow a track going up, which can be wet in places. Reach a stile and access a lane, at a corner.

4 Continue ahead on the lane for about 200 yards. At a passing place on the right, follow the footpath sign through a stile. The path goes to the left and reaches a metal kissing gate. Keep ahead on the narrow path, contouring

■ *The view across the valley* ■

along the rough hillside. Come to a gap, with a stone post and a fence to the right. This the start of a wood, and you go ahead through trees on a fine path. This is an enjoyable way to lose calories. Soon you see the stone wall of the **Deanhead churchyard**. Continue ahead to the church, which stands in a commanding position overlooking the reservoir. Spend time here, then continue the route on the green lane, to the left of the church, into an open area with houses around.

5 Look ahead for a footpath arrow pointing right. The path is a few yards below the grass area, in a corner by the front gate of a house. Here a narrow path starts; when you are on it a footpath sign confirms the route. Bear left in front of a small stone building. Now follow the path through trees, a well-walked, pleasant route and you could push yourself here. There is a notice explaining the **Styhill medieval settlement**. Beyond here at a path junction go ahead, not to the right. Soon the dam wall comes into view ahead.

6 Climb up to a high level stony track, which crosses the dam close to the motorway. When you have reached the end, follow the arrows to the right. You are at the car park level and as you meet a road, go right to the start.

10 *Fairburn Ings*

Nature, Reserved for All

■ *Birds aplenty at Main Bay* ■

Lakes and ponds left over from mine workings have now become the RSPB Nature Reserve at Fairburn Ings. This important wildlife sanctuary attracts large numbers of birds and there are viewing platforms and hides where visitors can see the wildlife close at hand. Binoculars will be useful. The route from the reserve goes through two agreeable villages, and there is some pleasant countryside in spite of the industrial areas around.

1 From the visitor centre, adorned with its attractive mosaic, go right and turn left at the sign to '**Riverbank Trail and Hides**'. Follow the boardwalk and turn left at the end, on the **Riverbank Trail**. Continue from a gate and the path climbs a little and goes through trees. You will hear birds in the trees and on the water; on the right is the **River Aire**. After about ¼ mile you reach the lake and see the **Bob Dickens Hide**, where birdwatchers can sit and watch the activity. **Village Bay Hide** is further on, then continue to a metal gate. The route turns left here, but before doing so it is interesting to make a short diversion, which is not too energetic. Go ahead on a path through the field and under the railway bridge ahead. There are steps going up to a walkway beside it, provided in 1922 for miners walking to work. From here you look over the wide river and **Ferrybridge power station** is of course clearly seen.

2 Retrace your steps, now going on the track signed to '**Cut Hide and Village Facilities**'. Leave the water and keep straight on, going uphill but nothing steep. Ignore stiles to the right and left of the path. Go up through a kissing gate and continue on a metalled lane into Fairburn village. Perhaps it is time for a rest, and you can study the displays at the horse trough and pump, which highlight aspects of the village. The old gaol is across the road to the right, where a cell was hewn into the soft limestone.

3 Go left from **Cut Road** for about 200 yards and turn right up **Beckfield Lane**. Further up a footpath sign indicates a right fork, up the lane. A gentle climb to rolling country follows, with no habitation and where no coal mining took place. Go through a kissing gate and along a field edge to a

GRADE: 2
ESTIMATED CALORIE BURN: 740

Description: A fine site for seeing wildlife, from where you walk through fields and woods.
Distance: 4¾ miles
Time: 3¼ hours
Gradient: Mostly level round the nature reserve, undulating from Fairburn village; 3 stiles.
Underfoot: The paths are generally good.
Starting point: The free car park at Fairburn Ings Nature Reserve. GR 451278. There are toilets at the visitor centre.
How to get there: One mile west of Fairburn village, which is on the A1246 off junction 42 of the A1(M).
OS map: Explorer 289 Leeds.
Refreshments: Limited choice on site. There is a pub in Fairburn.

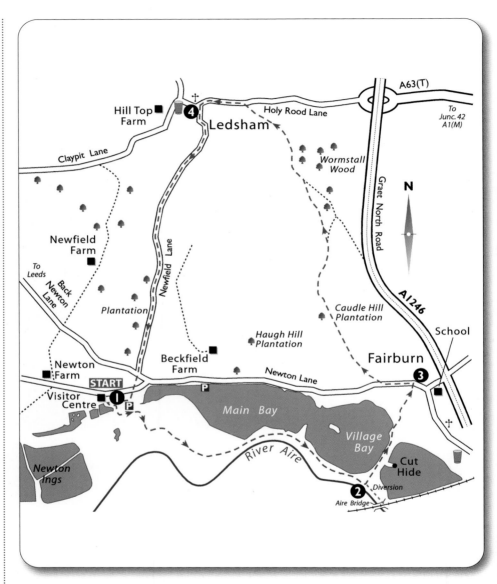

second gate. There are fine views to the west as you follow a track beside a fence by **Caudle Hill Plantation**. In the distance the village of **Ledsham** will be seen, which is your objective. At a point below power lines take the lower path, to the left and to a gate and a narrow strip of woodland. Go

■ *The old gaol in Fairburn village* ■

ahead over the bottom of a long field. Look for a wooden stile on the right. Here you leave the field and go into **Wormstall Wood**, walking along its edge. Leave the wood at a stile and reach a gate, where you join the road into **Ledsham**. Continue ahead; on the right is the old school dated 1769. Follow the road round the corner then ahead into **Newfield Lane**.

4 There are south-facing seats outside the church, which has interesting features, and more of the village up the road if you wish to see it. As you set off down **Newfield Lane**, the return to the start involves a walk of about 1¼ miles. Bear left, away from **Manor Garth**. Follow this bridleway south, which soon becomes unsurfaced. You climb gradually, going between open fields at first. Later you walk beside a long plantation as the land slopes down. The route is quite direct and the lakes of **Fairburn Ings** come into view as you descend through trees. Reach a road and go a little left, then right and over a field. Cross a road to reach the entrance to the nature reserve to complete the route.

11 Ilkley
To the Cow and Calf Rocks

■ *The Cow and Calf Rocks above Ilkley* ■

There must be a visit to Ilkley Moor in this book. Try this walk when you feel ready; to complete it successfully your health needs to be in good order. Rocks are a feature of this fairly strenuous route. Some paths involve scrambling, using your hands to help with obstacles such as stones and boulders. Both routes include the trickier paths, and the Cow and Calf Rocks. At White Wells there are deep plunge baths, dating from the 18th century, with a café. The longer route gives views of the western parts of the moor, and even more exercise!

1 At the car park you see the Charles Darwin connection with Ilkley. Features nearby include the **Millennium Green** and **Maze**.

To start the walk, below the cattle grid, briefly turn into **Crossbeck Road** and go immediately by the fence to two footpath signs. Follow the left one, going up a surfaced path. Ignore a sign pointing slightly left and keep on the path up to the **Tarn**. Go along the left bank to the far end of the lake. By a seat go up steps onto a narrow, but clear, moorland path. It is about a 30 minute walk to the **Cow and Calf Rocks**, which you may see ahead and above you. The path is stony and through bracken, on a well-walked route that climbs then descends to cross a footbridge. Bear left up large steps, then on a section with a narrower path. Continue over a green track that crosses your path. Climb a little, before contouring round the hillside. Aim to walk in between the **Cow** and **Calf** themselves. Follow a stone paved path, up to a wider paved path. You are at the entrance to **Hangingstones Quarry**, where you may see climbers about.

2 Descend on the wider path a few yards, then turn right on the narrower paved path going up the hillside. When it finishes go up a little further to a grassy triangle; some level ground may be welcome, but there is still some uphill work. Take a green track going left. Continue at a fork, the left track

---

GRADE: 2
ESTIMATED CALORIE BURN: 480/760

Description: A walk round some features of Yorkshire's best-known moor.
Distance: 3 or 5 miles
Time: 2½ or 3½ hours
Gradient: Plenty of ups to reach the moorland, with not much level walking.
Underfoot: Easier paths on the second half. A stream to cross without a bridge. No stiles.
Starting point: Darwin Gardens free car park, Wells Road, Ilkley. GR 117471.
How to get there: At the traffic lights on the A65 in the centre of Ilkley, turn up into Brook Street. At the crossroads, go over slightly left, then up Wells Road to the cattle grid and you will find the car park on the right. There is a good train service.
OS map: Explorer 297 Lower Wharfedale & Washburn Valley.
Refreshments: At the Cow and Calf Rocks and White Wells.

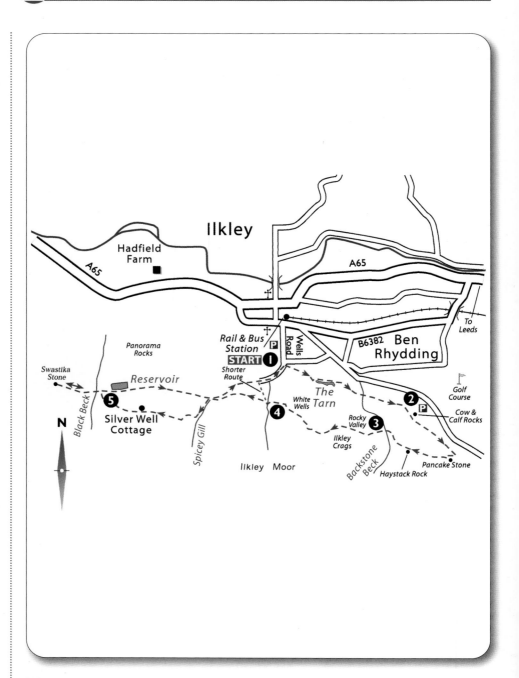

Ilkley

Hadfield Farm

A65

A65

Panorama Rocks

Swastika Stone

Reservoir

Black Beck

5

Silver Well Cottage

N

Spicey Gill

Ilkley Moor

Rail & Bus Station

START ①

Shorter Route

Wells Road

White Wells

The Tarn

④

B6382

Ben Rhydding

To Leeds

Golf Course

②

Cow & Calf Rocks

Rocky Valley

③

Ilkley Crags

Backstone Beck

Haystack Rock

Pancake Stone

■ *Heather in bloom on the moor* ■

going to the hotel. You have completed one mile hereabouts. After 200 yards reach a junction where a path goes down to the left. Follow the narrow path to the right. Your objective is in sight – the large boulder protruding over the cliff above, known as the Pancake Stone. Do not go directly up, instead walk ahead beyond it on a rising path and turn right at a crossroads of paths. Continue up a green path and climb the last few feet to the ridge, probably with relief. The weathered top of the Pancake Stone is covered with cups and rings dating from around 500 BC. A few feet behind the stone, walk west on a track along the ridge. Cross a track in a dip, and reach the large isolated Haystack Rock, which has carvings from 1400 to 800 BC. Join a wide, stony track, which you follow for less than 200 yards, to a junction where your path goes off to the right, as though heading to Ilkley. Go down and meet another track and turn left to a stream, Backstone Beck. There is no bridge to cross it by but the large boulders should suffice. This is a popular area and the views around are excellent.

55

3 From the stream walk on the lower, rutted path. This goes up, towards a valley ahead with the rocks of **Ilkley Crags** above. You suddenly stop going up and descend into the spectacular **Rocky Valley**. It is a good experience to walk through, with the huge boulders scattered around. As the path becomes easier, a track joins from the left, at a **Millennium Way** sign. Keep ahead, walking down on a good track. Go right to **White Wells** – if the flag is flying the café is open! There are toilets close by.

4 Leave **White Wells** on the white chalky path and cross a stream, as the track bends. In a few yards there is a turn left on a moorland path. *Here the routes divide.*

For the shorter route, continue down the track. Go right on the road, and after **Brodrick Drive** turn left towards the car park.

To continue the longer route, follow the moorland path between bracken, and towards the end climb to join a road. Go left on this and follow it steeply up, round bends and beside **Spicey Gill**, for about ½ mile. The gradient should help the calorie burn. Where the road becomes unsurfaced, a footpath sign points right along a track. Go ahead on it and pass **Silver Well Cottage**, continuing to a footpath gate. Follow a path away, with fine views of the reservoir below and the **Wharfe valley** towards **Bolton Abbey** and beyond. Gradually head down to trees before the stream ahead, **Black Beck**, where there is a pleasant spot to sit. Do not cross the stream unless you want to visit the famous **Swastika Stone**, which is ¼ mile further on over the bridge

5 *To continue the walk,* turn towards **Ilkley**, following the edge of the moor, near the houses. Cross a stone bridge and continue down the road. Go right at the junction, seeing **White Wells** above. After **Brodrick Drive** turn left towards the car park.

■ *Central Park in Haworth* ■

Cross a stile and ignore a left turn to a footbridge. Pass through a kissing gate and continue on a varied path. The metal posts across the path are boundary markers. From a footbridge you see **Haworth** ahead, a bit industrial at first. Reach a road and go left, then right on **Station Road** to **Haworth station**.

■ *Look out for me as you walk* ■

There is still some coal mining industry in this area but much of the visible workings have now gone. In their place the land is being made green, and the country park between Ackworth Moor Top and Fitzwilliam is still developing. There are plenty of trees planted and now nature is beginning to take over. The result is a pleasing open aspect with space to roam. Ackworth Moor Top is not a place that is going to dress up for you, but its immediate countryside is very pleasant and any small town with a walking route through its centre like the Dando Way would be proud.

1 From the **Angel** turn right in the car park to a fence crossing. Go left and down through the tunnel under the road. The path is unsurfaced and you reach a barrier. Go ahead, past a seat, to a signpost by the road. Go left briefly on the road to a metal sculpture of a dog. You are entering the **Fitzwilliam Country Park**, which was once a mining area. Go along the track, with the trees on the right. Keep along here for about a mile and reach a lake. Hereabouts you could spend time exploring the country park. Ahead you will be aware of trains going to **Fitzwilliam station**. Pass the car park and see **Wentworth Terrace**.

2 *If you are starting the walk at **Fitzwilliam station***, leave from the Leeds arrival platform by the ramp and cross the road.

The entrance to **Fitzwilliam Country Park** is found over the road from **Wentworth Terrace**. Look for the footpath sign and the metal sculpture by Harry Malkin. Follow the gravelled path and join another path, bearing left. Go along for a little over ¼ mile with young trees about. At a junction of paths where your track turns right, go left to a gravelled area. The end of a road and a fenced business park is to the left. Go right on an unsurfaced path and through a barrier. The path descends beside the country park with fields on the left. When the lane bends right, ignore a stile on the left and keep on to reach a road at a wide junction. Follow it to the left as it becomes an urban street. Reach the main road in an area known as **Brackenhill**.

GRADE: 2
ESTIMATED CALORIE BURN: 760

Description: An interesting area to walk in.
Distance: 5 miles
Time: 3½ hours
Gradient: The land is gently undulating; 4 stiles.
Underfoot: Generally good.
Starting point: The Angel pub, on the main road at Ackworth Moor Top, GR 431163. Park in the pub car park if you intend to patronise the pub or park on-street. Alternatively, Fitzwilliam rail station if you come by train, GR 415153, starting the walk at point 2.
How to get there: Ackworth Moor Top is on the A638 Wakefield to Doncaster road. Buses run from Wakefield; trains from Leeds to Fitzwilliam station.
OS map: Explorer 278 Sheffield & Barnsley.
Refreshments: At the Angel pub.

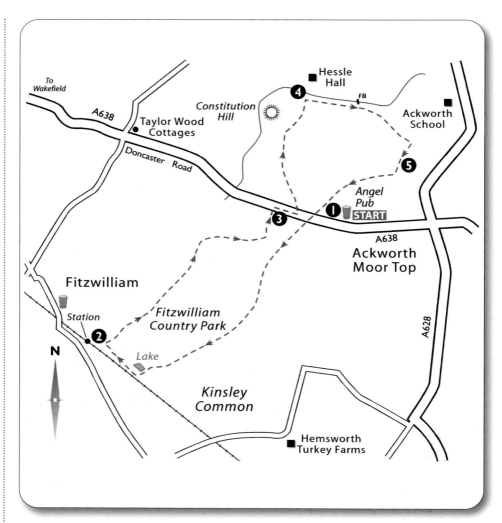

3 Cross over and go right. Take the next turn after **Hayfield Way**, at a footpath sign to the left. Go through new houses, then past industrial areas. The lane continues to buildings at **Constitution Hill** on the left. Go ahead on a narrow path to a stile. Walk down a long field and at the bottom a right of way crosses from left to right.

4 The route continues to the right through a kissing gate. Before that, you can go through the gate on the left and along the paved path to a

■ *Firm paths speed you on your way* ■

footbridge, which is a pleasant spot. Return across the field and from the kissing gate follow a path by the stream, with fields on your right. After about ¼ mile reach a small concrete footbridge over the stream. A few yards ahead you leave the streamside path. A path goes off right and follows beside a hedge on the left, with fields on the right. At the end of the hedge join a track coming from the left. Go right and up to the top, where you reach houses and a road at **Mount Pleasant**.

5 Go across and through a barrier, and ahead over a field to a second barrier. Before the houses you turn right on a surfaced path. This is the walkway known as the '**Dando Way**'. Named after a former local councillor, this pleasant urban route is followed as it winds through **Ackworth Moor Top** for about ½ mile. You approach the tunnel and the **Angel pub** is immediately left, before the path goes down.

*If you started the walk at **Fitzwilliam station**, continue under the tunnel at point 1 to return.*

■ *The Calder & Hebble Navigation Canal* ■

Mirfield is an unpretentious town, still dealing in textiles to some extent, which was once the mainstay industry in these parts. An attractive place to start from, it is in a central position in the county and easily reached from other parts of West Yorkshire. South of the town, the countryside is surprisingly good. Mirfield has the merit of both the River Calder and the Calder and Hebble Navigation Canal passing through, and there are always things to see by waterways.

1 Leave the road and walk east, along the path with the canal on your left, on a quiet stretch. **Brewery Wharf** is behind you, further down the road. There are industrial sites on the right and the opposite bank is tree-lined. Technically this part of the **Calder and Hebble** is the **Mirfield Cut**. There is a ¾ mile walk to **Shepley Bridge Lock** where the canal joins the **Calder**. There are seats where you may watch people messing about in boats, but don't say that to them.

2 Leave by the gate and go over the bridge across the canal. Turn right carefully on a traffic road that crosses the river, with traffic lights at each end. When you are over you see the **Ship Inn** ahead, and a public footpath sign points left. Go through the pub car park to a footpath sign, confirmation that this is the right of way. Follow the path ahead, which is paved in places, between the river and lakes. When a path goes off up to the right, keep by the river. The railway line is reached, a busy trans-Pennine route. After about 300 yards, take a turn to the right. Go up stone steps – there is an archway on the right – to the railway level. It is possible to miss this turn, just before a lock across the river where a canal section enters, the **Greenwood Cut**.

3 Turn left beside the railway fence and cross a wide bridge over the line. Continue ahead through a barrier into a wood and keep on this track. On

GRADE: 2
ESTIMATED CALORIE BURN: 760

Description: Walking through woods and by water.
Distance: 5 miles
Time: 3½ hours
Gradient: Fairly steep after a level start, with a steady descent; 8 stiles.
Underfoot: Many paths are paved, but be prepared for some muddy sections after rain.
Starting point: At the canal bridge in Station Road, Mirfield. Between the A644, Huddersfield Road, and the railway station. On-road parking is available nearby, and there are toilets. GR 204196.
How to get there: Mirfield is 3 miles from Dewsbury, on the A644. There is a rail service between Leeds, Huddersfield and Wakefield.
OS map: Explorer 288 Bradford & Huddersfield.
Refreshments: In Mirfield. There are pubs en route, and an ice cream parlour at Whitley Lower (see point 5).

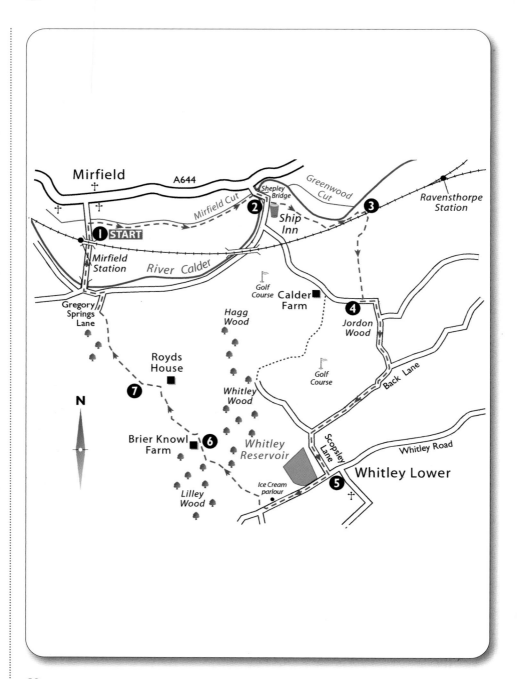

■ *The golf course passed on the way* ■

the left a series of paths are being laid out. Keep by an impressive new fence up a stone path, until you emerge out of the woodland and continue up. At the top follow the path right a few yards.

4 Turn sharp left and take a narrow path for the width of one field. At a junction turn right up a path marked with a carved bridleway sign. Now follow this old paved path for ¾ mile on a steady climb, which should provide exercise. It is mostly enclosed by walls with long paved sections, but may be muddy. Ignore paths turning off, and as you climb there are good views across the golf course. Perhaps you will be relieved when the surface changes to a metalled lane and you are nearly done with climbing. Go ahead, and left along an urban street, **Scopsley Lane**. Reach the main road with the **Woolpack Inn** on the left.

5 Turn right on the road, past houses. The **Whitley Reservoir** marked on the OS map is above you, with an OS trig point, which the map indicates as a height of 173 metres. How does the water reach the highest point in the district? Beyond is **Charlotte's ice cream parlour**, then continue to a white house and a footpath going right. There is a seat. Go down the side of the house to a gap stile, then follow by a hedge and fence to a wooden stile. Continue down the field to the bottom corner and through a stile, in a ditch, into the wood. There is a pleasant path down through trees, then reach a stile by a metal gate. Walk down beside the wall and through a sunken section to a gate, with a smaller gate for walkers.

6 Go along a green section, then to **Brier Knowl Farm**. Go to the left between buildings, over a cattle grid and walk away to the right down a drive. Leave it when you reach a wall. On the left a few yards away, go through a gate and down steps, and a fairly steep descent by a wall. Continue at a stile and a gate and bear right on a narrow path. On the right a cricket ground is seen below, in front of **Royds House**. Be ready to leave the path, at a wooden stile on the left; a post has four arrows on it. Cross the field, to a stile by the right of the trees ahead. **Mirfield parish church tower** is prominent in the distance.

7 Continue down to the bottom of the hill, by the wall and a fence. Walk diagonally across the field to the wood, where an arrow points right. Keep by the wood down to the bottom left corner, avoiding boggy land to the right. Reach a stile and an enclosed path behind an area of houses. Turn right onto **Gregory Springs Lane**, then left on a motor road. Take the next turn right, where you cross the **Calder**. Ahead you will see the railway bridge. Continue to the station, or the canal bridge or into **Mirfield**.

16 *Bingley St Ives*

The Saints Go Marching In

■ *A lunchtime viewpoint* ■

Bingley is unusual in having a main road, a bypass, a railway, a canal and a river – all close together – passing through its centre. This makes it an interesting place, and when you cross the River Aire the St Ives Estate is a popular place to walk. This land was given to the people of Bingley by the Ferrand family in the 1920s and it provides plenty of variety, with carved wooden figures hiding in the trees and elsewhere. Do the walk also for the fine view from the Druid's Altar.

1 Enter **Myrtle Park** and bear left before the flower beds and war memorial. Go down paths along the left hand edge of the park to the river. Cross the green footbridge and continue on the path. Turn right on the lane to houses, going right at **Templar Cottage**. This attractive area is **Beck Foot**. Cross the stone packhorse bridge and go through a gap on the right. Bear left round to a wall gap, then head up a track. Continue past properties and walk away up a lane to a road junction, requiring care.

2 Cross straight over the busy **Harden road**. From the steps bear left for more climbing, up the wooded hillside on a rougher track. Reach a signpost, where you continue up to a road. Go right on it and keep on this as it bends left past a car park. You have walked about a mile. There is a straighter section – you could increase your pace to get your heart working. Pass a play area on the right and toilets.

3 Follow the road to the right, then you pass **St Ives Golf Club**. Ahead is a tea room, but it's too early to stop yet! Beyond here leave the metalled road to walk by the picturesque **Coppice Pond**. There is a bird hide to see, as you continue up the unsurfaced track for ½ mile. After a good climb, an opening in the trees reveals **Lady Blantyre's Rock**.

4 You can look around here and read the memorial to William Busfield

GRADE: 2
ESTIMATED CALORIE BURN: 780

Description: An energetic walk in woodland and open land.
Distance: 5¼ miles
Time: 3½ hours
Gradient: A long gradual walk up to a high point overlooking the Aire valley, then descending; 4 stiles.
Underfoot: About one mile of quiet road walking, otherwise unsurfaced tracks.
Starting point: Myrtle Park, Bingley, the entrance near Bingley Pool. GR 107390. Toilets nearby.
How to get there: Bingley is on the A650 between Bradford and Keighley. There are pay & display car parks near the start. Regular trains to Bingley on the Airedale line.
OS map: Explorer 288 Bradford & Huddersfield.
Refreshments: Local pubs and cafés.

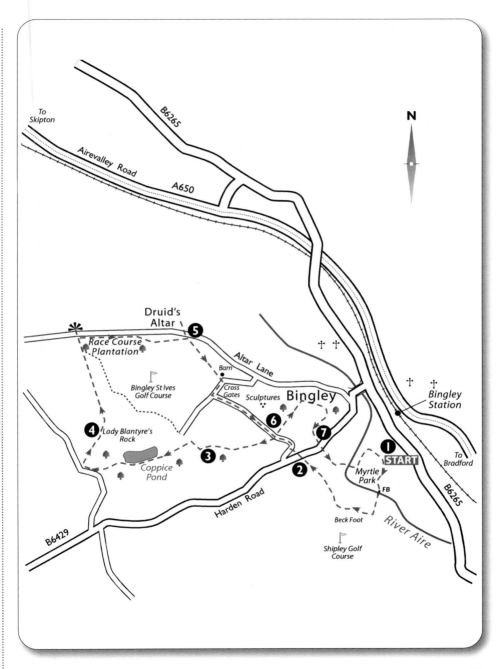

■ *One of the wooden sculptures in the St Ives Estate* ■

Ferrand's mother-in-law. The stone obelisk commemorates William. Continue the uphill gradient on the track, which soon follows by a straight wall. As you progress, the golf course is around you. At the top reach a kissing gate in a stone wall. The route turns right just **before** this gate, on a wide track through trees. However, you can go forward, through the gate, for a fine view of **Airedale**. This is the highest point of the walk, though it is not necessarily all downhill from here! Return and take the path, with the wall on your left at first. You are descending gradually in a pleasant area – when the rhododendrons are in bloom it is a wonderful place. The path winds round and goes down by the edge of the wood to another kissing gate. Your route will continue off to the right on the wide, walled lane, but first there is a diversion to the **Druid's Altar**.

5 Go left and through the gap to an open area. Ignore the two turnings to the left and go ahead on the narrow path through trees into a grassy area. Ahead reach a rocky edge. These flat-topped rocks are known as the **Druid's Altar**, from where you look down on the valley below, with a sense of achievement. When you are ready, return through the gap to the wide lane. Walk between its walls and reach a long ruined stone barn on your left, at an area known as **Cross Gates**. The lane bears right and you turn next left on **Blind Lane**. Follow this down to a gate and you may recognise the place from earlier in the walk.

6 This time go left on the footpath signed into the wood, which has several wood carvings you can look for, created by Rodney Holland. The route keeps up on the main track to a T-junction, at a picnic table. Behind, the land drops steeply. Turn right and follow the path down and up. Soon you must take a left turn. Shortly after a snake carving, as the path goes right, there is a picnic table on the left. Twenty yards beyond, a minor path descends through trees. This turning is well before a wall and a gate leading to a car park. The path winds down to a wall corner. Go down half-right a few yards, where a second path joins from the right. Descend steeply to the road below, at a signpost. Take care here.

7 Beware of fast traffic, and cross directly over to a gap. Follow a footpath down, with many steps. As it bends left, look to the right for a footbridge into **Myrtle Park**. Cross the grass half-left to the flight of steps. This final climb is perhaps a sting in the tale, but hopefully you are up to it. Follow a path, passing a play area, and look for the flower beds once more. As you exit the park, the name **Thrift Way** has obvious connections with the famous building society HQ nearby!

With a Spring in Your Step

■ *The long weir on the River Wharfe* ■

When a chalybeate spring was discovered beside the River Wharfe in 1744, the village of Boston Spa became well known for the treatments offered to those afflicted with ailments. However, as other spas prospered Boston's declined. In the end the village was left with the remains of the baths, which you see on the walk, and the Spa name. Nowadays it is a prosperous village, with the Thorp Arch trading estate across the river. Once a military location, this is the site of Leeds United's training ground, the British Library, and a prison!

following a footpath through trees. Rejoin the track in open land. Reach a junction with a turn left to **Micklefield**. The signpost says you are at **Bragdale**, and there is a seat.

2 This unfenced track between fields has wide views. There is some climbing and maybe you can press on here, to eat up the calories. The motorway on your right is mostly hidden. Continue ahead at a junction, by a seat. The track winds down, beside the motorway, and joins a metalled lane. Follow this and cross the motorway bridge. Keep on the lane to the road in the village of **Micklefield**.

3 Cross over, noting the **Blands Arms**, following the public footpath on the right of the school. Turn left at the fence corner, and down a narrower path, labelled '**New Path**' on the signpost at the end. Take the semi-rural track signed '**Lower Peckfield Lane**', with sports fields on the left. Cross the railway, with care, and turn left. The former Peckfield Colliery occupied this area, and a mining memorial stands opposite a business park. Walk down the road to the main street, with the railway station opposite.
*If you started at **Micklefield**, reach the station to complete the walk.*
*If you have started at **Lotherton Hall**, cross the road and turn right.*

GRADE: 3
ESTIMATED CALORIE BURN: 950

Description: Fields and woodland, between the Lotherton Estate and Micklefield.
Distance: 6¼ miles
Time: 4½ hours
Gradient: Gradual ups and downs.
Underfoot: Country paths contrast with urban surfaces; no stiles.
Starting point: The Stable Courtyard at Lotherton Hall, GR 449361. Alternatively, Micklefield station if you come by rail, GR 445327, starting at point 4 and allowing around 1½ hours from Lotherton Hall to return for a train.
How to get to Lotherton Hall: Leave the M1 at junction 47 and take the B1217 north-east for 2½ miles. Parking charge. Trains to Micklefield from Leeds.
OS map: Explorer 289 Leeds.
Refreshments: The Stable Courtyard and the Blands Arms in Micklefield.

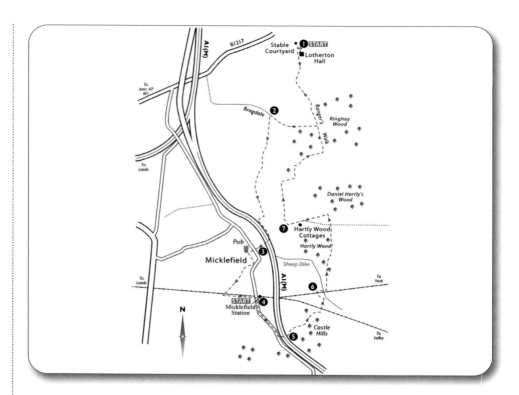

4 *If you are starting the walk at **Micklefield station**,* turn left from it onto the main street.

Both routes walk up the main street. Pass a row of houses, named at the end **Prospect Terrace**. Walk out of the village, past the speed de-restriction and village signs. Turn next left and through gates onto a closed road going under the motorway. Walk up to reach a gate, where you access a wood.

5 Now start a woodland walk with a left turn a few yards ahead, then along a track through trees. Soon reach a post signed as '**Castle Hills**', and go left down a narrower footpath. Continue ahead and pass a steep dip on the left, then reach a crossing of the Leeds–Selby railway. There is a good sightline – but take care. The path continues through the wood, bearing left down to a bridge where you go under the Leeds–York railway. After the bridge find a seat and a signpost.

6 Turn right and head towards the wooded area. Cross a small stream, **Sheep**

■ *Approaching the Lotherton Estate* ■

Dike, and enter **Hartly Wood**. This name appears with and without an 'e'. Follow the main path up through the wood, which is mostly clear and waymarked. You walk near the edge of the wood and reach a seat at a junction of paths. Go ahead here, on a 'permissive' path, not marked on the OS map. Continue close to the edge of the wood, reaching open land and a yellow post. You are following the boundary of West Yorkshire here; hopefully you will feel that the effort is rewarding. Go ahead to the next wood corner, and a seat. Turn left onto a track between fields, towards **Hartly Wood Cottages**. There are kennels here and a wind turbine. Continue past and soon see a signpost pointing right.

7 Follow this field track and an area of woodland comes into sight, marked **'Weet Wood'** on the OS map. When you reach it, turn right and find a seat. Now follow a track, which skirts the woodland, with large fields of barley growing, if the season is right. After ½ mile a sign points left and into the wood. The path through is **Ranger's Walk** and is another contrast to the open fields. Keep straight through the wood, to a junction.
If you started at Lotherton Hall, you will recognise this as the way you went earlier. Continue ahead on the path you have already used to Lotherton, to complete the walk.

*If you have started at **Micklefield Station**,* you will need this turn when you return from **Lotherton Hall**. Keep ahead towards the **Lotherton Estate** through gates and leave the wood. Follow a field path by trees up towards the buildings ahead. From a metal gap carry on to a footpath gate and into the grounds of Lotherton Hall, to **Stable Courtyard**. When you are ready, start your return to **Micklefield** at point 1.

■ *The Kirklees Light Railway* ■

Bretton Country Park is an extensive landscape, containing the Yorkshire Sculpture Park, an outdoor setting for works by sculptors including Henry Moore, Barbara Hepworth and Antony Gormley. The official map guide is useful to identify what you see. When you have reached Clayton West on the longer walk, there is an option to visit the Kirklees Light Railway. This 15-inch narrow gauge line runs to Shelley on a picturesque 50 minute round trip. It operates at weekends, school holidays and all through August. Check before you go to the station (telephone: 01484 865727). If you do the walk, and add the train trip, you will have had a busy day. The shorter walk is based mainly on the area of the country park.

1 From the car park go through a kissing gate on the left of the information kiosk, signed '**Barnsley Boundary Walk**' and '**Wakefield Way**'. Follow the path, then turn right after a few yards and go next left, on the **Wakefield Way**. Take this long green track, and from **Dam Head Bridge** you keep the stream on the left. The sculptures are set around the parkland and **Bretton Hall** is above. Reach a long fence and go through a gate, continuing by the stream. You are now on the **Dearne Way**. At the next fence go through a gate, slightly right. The **Cascade Bridge** is below.

2 *For the shorter walk,* first admire the lake view from the bridge. Then walk back up the track and through an iron gateway. Continue up to a sign pointing to **Clayton West**. Just beyond, go through a wooden gate on the right into the park, at point 6.

For the longer walk, go left and cross the bridges, where the scene is one of interest on the water. See the striking *One and Other* by Antony Gormley as you continue up on the track. Go straight on, not to the **Longside Gallery**. Now you are climbing, away from the park and it will mean you are burning calories. Follow the track to a stile in the fence on the right. Go over and cross the large field. Aim for the left hand edge of the line of trees on the right, where you find a stile. From here descend to a stile at a road.

3 Go over to a stile a few yards left. Walk down the field to a hedge corner –

GRADE: 3
ESTIMATED CALORIE BURN: 360/1000

Description: Through parkland and on field paths to Clayton West.
Distance: 2½ or 6 miles. Add 1¼ miles on the longer walk to visit the Kirklees Light Railway.
Time: 1½ hours for the shorter walk; 3½ hours for the longer option, or 5 hours minimum if including the train trip.
Gradient: A ridge to climb to Clayton West; 20 stiles.
Underfoot: Varied terrain and the paths are generally good.
Starting point: Bretton Country Park pay & display car park, not the main entrance car park. Toilets here. GR 295124.
How to get there: The car park is reached on the A637 and is ½ mile north of junction 38 on the M1.
OS maps: Explorer 278 Sheffield & Barnsley and 288 Bradford & Huddersfield.
Refreshments: In the park.

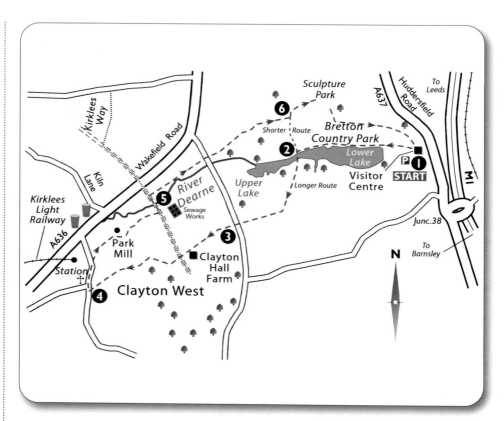

views of the **Emley Moor TV mast** are prominent. Go up beside a hedge to a stile before **Clayton Hall Farm** and onto a track. Pass on the right of the farmyard and walk away on a track to a junction, near a new house. Go straight on at a stile marked **Kirklees Way** (KW). Follow the hedge to a stile, then down a field, **KW** direction, to a wooden stile. Continue down to a stile just ahead. Go down by a hedge and cross a stream, and continue by a hedge to its end. There is a **KW** sign and stile. Continue up to a further stile into the **Kayes Millennium Green**, with a 'spiral history' of **Clayton West**. From a black gate follow the track to a road in the village.

4 *For the **Kirklees Light Railway**, there is a nearly ¾ mile walk there and back, as it is not accessed directly from this road. Go down to **Church Lane**, and up it to a right turn into **Victoria Street**. Turn into **Victoria Terrace**, then **Albert Street**. At the bottom go right on the main road and right before the railway bridge to the station.*

■ *One of the many sculptures in the country park* ■

To continue the main route, go right and down the road, past **The Royds** and take the next turning right, **Back Lane**. Pass a recreation ground and keep on the lane, ignoring turnings off. After **Park Mill** on the left, take a left fork and continue to a T-junction at **Clayton West treatment works**. Turn left and cross the **River Dearne** at a bridge. A little further on find a stile on the right in the hedge.

5 Cross the long field to the far corner, and a stile by a large tree. Turn right to another stile, then enjoy a riverside walk. In the wall ahead cross a stile a little to the left. Go over a road and continue to a gap stile by a metal gate. The **Dearne Way** is signed through a picturesque area. Keep on the track, which curves left to a footbridge, crossing **Bentley Brook**. Now a climb is needed, half-left up the hill on a narrow path. From a stile at the top follow the arrow over a field and on a path beside a hedge. At a T-junction, with a boundary wall of the **Sculpture Park** ahead, **Clayton West** is signed as 1¾ miles back. Turn left briefly on the track.

6 *The shorter walk joins here.* The **Sculpture Park** is accessed through a wooden gate on the right. The various buildings and galleries are situated nearby and the official map guide identifies the sites. The return to the car park is still a mile away, but it is a pleasant stroll to complete the walk.

■ *On the path through the Harewood Estate* ■

If you are ready for the challenge of the longest route in this book, Golden Acre Park is a gateway to walks in several directions. You walk to the Harewood Estate, where red kites have been released in a scheme to reintroduce these birds into Yorkshire. Paths through the estate also give a glimpse of an *Emmerdale* set. Golden Acre Park is noted for its attractive gardens and trees. The shorter route still provides a challenging circuit, without going to Harewood.

1 From the car park, cross the A660 by the underpass and turn left into **Golden Acre Park**. Follow the signs to the café and toilets, just below is an area with seats.

To start the walk, continue on a path alongside a miniature railway track. Carry on through the trees and approach the park boundary fence. The lake is seen below, and you continue at a sign for the **Leeds Country Way** (LCW). Just ahead go through a small gate in a large hedge, slightly off the path. Leave the park and turn left onto the rough track. Go up to a junction of two roads.

2 Cross the first road and walk along the side of the road ahead, **King Lane**, passing the entrance to **Clonmore Farm**. Reach a stile and go left into a wood. Walk through, mostly following the left hand edge. About halfway along a notice describes this area, **Eccup Whin**. Continue along the woodland edge and leave at a gap, turning left onto **Black Hill Lane**.

3 Follow the road for ¼ mile and go down **Swan Lane**. At a T-junction turn right through a kissing gate and walk parallel with **Lineham Farm** buildings to a second gate. Cross the long field to a wall stile, then veer slightly right to a lone tree. An arrow points the way ahead on a track. Reach a wooden step stile at a metal gate. You cross **Eller Beck** and walk up the grass to a wall stile.

GRADE: 3
ESTIMATED CALORIE BURN: 760/1100

Description: Testing routes in the countryside north of Leeds.
Distance: 5 or 8 miles
Time: 3½ or 5½ hours
Gradient: Undulating land; 11 stiles on both routes.
Underfoot: A variety of paths; about 1½ miles of road walking on the longer route, ¾ mile on the shorter route.
Starting point: Golden Acre Park café area. GR 267418.
How to get there: The park is 6 miles north-west of Leeds on the A660. Park in the free car park on the left-hand side of the A660 as one drives north. The X84 Leeds to Otley bus passes.
OS map: Explorer 297 Lower Wharfedale and Washburn Valley.
Refreshments: There is a café in the park. The New Inn in Eccup Lane at point 4 of the walk also welcomes walkers.

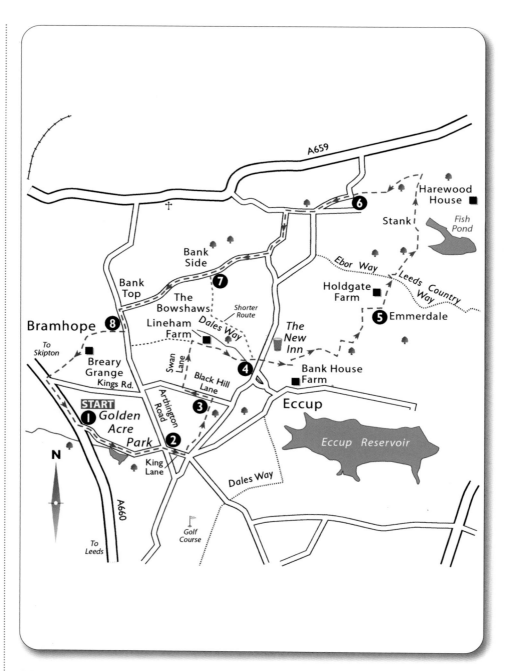

4 *The routes divide here. The shorter route turns off left,* before the wall stile and through the wooden stile on the left. This crosses an area known as **The Bowshaws** and is part of a **Dales Way Link** route. From the wooden stile reach a stile by a gate. Follow the field edge to a corner stile; go ahead to a signpost and right down the field edge. Continue through stiles and reach **Bank Side**. Go down a track for a few yards and turn left to a gate below an iron barn, where the longer route joins from the right at point 7.

The longer route continues ahead, through the wall stile to Eccup Lane – beware of traffic. Cross slightly left to a stile and go over two fields. Turn left onto part of the **LCW**, a route encircling the city. It is about 1 mile to the **Harewood Estate**, walking a section mostly enclosed by walls and hedges with sharp turns. At one stage the route opens out into a large field, keep following the right hand edge. Look out for red kites. The last section goes down a field and bends right to meet a track. A green notice shows you are at the renowned **Harewood Estate**. Over 3 miles completed!

5 Go left; the slightly hidden collection of houses is a set for *Emmerdale*. Pass **Holdgate Farm** and continue through trees to a junction of five paths. Take the public bridleway, going left and down. The sunken path curves to the right; it is signed to a gate by a stone house. **Harewood House** may just be seen above the trees and the lake is nearby. Continue up after the cattle grid and reach houses at **Stank**. Bear slightly left and cross a stream. Continue up a wide track, with a business area on the right. At a junction go sharply left. You have covered about 4¼ miles and are now turning towards **Golden Acre**. Deer may be seen on the right as you walk down an unsurfaced lane and cross a cattle grid. Continue over a stream, following signs indicating 'bridleway' and 'way out'. Leave **Harewood** and reach a road.

6 Keep on past the houses, with a pavement, then some road walking. Keep along this road, with a wood on the right, continuing at a junction. Turn left opposite a house on the right, down a lane. Pass **Tinker Close** and continue to **Allums Lane**. Follow this, on the **Ebor Way**, without habitation, until you reach **Bank Side** about ½ mile on. Do not approach this property; instead go ahead slightly left to a gate by an iron barn.

7 *The shorter route joins here.* Both routes continue on a high track, with wide views of the **Wharfe valley**, to **Bank Top**, a second property. Keep left of the buildings and exit by the drive, turning left. After 300 yards see a footpath gate on the right, off the road, well before **Breary Grange**.

■ *Golden Acre Park* ■

8 This path is a diversion, and is clearly marked, along the fence and through gates. Go half-left across a field to a ladder stile by an oak tree. Continue ahead over a field, to a stile by the A660 roundabout at **Bramhope**. Go left and cross **Kings Road** onto the pavement by the main road. Ahead is **Golden Acre**; look for the milestone marking the distance to London, very precisely! Reach the park and go through the gate.